# Contents

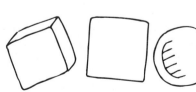

# Introduction

This book has been written to support early years providers in their planning and implementation of the mathematics curriculum, in the particular area of shape, size and position. It provides an extensive and varied range of activities that will inspire young children while supporting practitioners in their quest to provide a broad and balanced curriculum. This book, along with the other books in this series, aims to help practitioners provide the young children in their settings with the best possible foundation to set them on the path to further successful learning.

### Early Learning Goals

The activities in this book develop aspects of the Early Learning Goals for Mathematics published by QCA. By drawing out specific details from the described Goals, the activities in this book offer practical ways of ensuring that the recommended curriculum for learning shape, size and position is comprehensively covered.

However, most of the activities will also extend learning in Language and Literacy and Personal and Social Development, as well as in many other mathematical areas, including counting, comparing, sorting, matching, ordering and simple recording. Other books in this series focus more precisely on particular mathematical aspects. These are *Numbers to 5* and *Numbers to 10*.

The ideas in this book can be applied equally well to the guidance documents on pre-school education published for Wales, Scotland and Northern Ireland.

### Baseline Assessment

Baseline Assessments must now be made for each 'rising five' child within their first half term in school reception classes. These assessments provide information on each child's knowledge, understanding and ability on entering school and can be used as the basis from which to measure progression over time. The information given also helps staff to plan according to each child's individual needs.

### Finding out what children know

Children will bring with them a range of different previous knowledge and experience. It will be helpful if you know this before you plan your work. It will enable you to match your questioning and tasks more carefully to each individual.

You can discover this by:
● Letting them play with different 2-D shapes and checking how many names they know. (Can they pick up the shapes you suggest?)
● Joining in construction play with building blocks and checking if they know the names and how different solids can be used. (Can they select the 3-D item you want? Do they know if it will balance and why?)
● Finding out if a child can count orally. (Is it by rote or with understanding?)
● Checking if they can relate numbers to objects or spaces on a board game. (Observe them playing; can they count out a number you request?)
● Checking if they can put jigsaw pieces where you ask them to.

● Seeing if they can put dolls' house furniture where you suggest. (In, high, low, behind and so on.)

● Checking if they can lay the table or engage in home play, putting objects as you direct or describing where they choose to place them.

● Checking if they can put things in size order. (Can they clear up/arrange things in the order you ask?)

Many of these initial assessments can be made by staff involved in observing – or better still, interacting with the child during planned play sessions.

## How to use this book

The activities in this book use simple, everyday materials found readily in early years' settings. The tasks are enjoyable and active and are linked closely to play. They are designed to be easily managed by staff. Each activity is supported by a photocopiable sheet with specific tasks to consolidate learning, and to help staff assess the children's level of understanding, which in turn will help them to plan future work.

Where the children are required to write on the sheet, it is described as an 'Individual recording' and can be kept for assessment purposes, otherwise it is referred to as an 'Individual task'.

The activities are aimed at the average four-year-old with suggestions for simplifying and extending the task for younger and older children. Many of the activities will also provide useful and attractive work from the children which can be used for display.

## Home links

It is vitally important for young children that their parents and carers are involved in their education. Encourage parents to see themselves as partners in their child's learning by informing them about what their child is doing at nursery.

For each activity useful ideas on how home links can be developed to reinforce learning and strengthen home-school partnerships are included. This may involve parents in contributing items for a display or ways in which they can carry on investigations started with you, at home.

## Progression and assessment

The activities in this book are organized into three main sections – shape, size and position. These icons are used to denote whether the activity focuses on shape ▧, size ▤ or position ▥, to provide a quick reference. The sections can be tackled in the order they appear, or you can begin with whatever fits in best with your own programme. The activities in each section, however, have been planned to become progressively more demanding, building on previous experience and learning. Following them in sequence would enable you to cover a structured programme over time. Each activity has been carefully written to encourage the correct development of mathematical language and concepts.

Many of the activities lend themselves to repetition with groups of children at a later date, to reinforce learning or to help you assess how much progress has been made. Practical suggestions for how to make assessments and retain records are included for each activity.

## Skills development

At the back of the book you will find a Skills development chart. Photocopy it to form an individual record for each child. As you cover each element, complete and date the sections with the child. This will give you a profile of what is known and understood. The blank sections will indicate areas where further mathematical experience needs planning and undertaking. Additionally, the chart will also serve as useful evidence of the breadth of work covered in your mathematical provision.

# Spin the shape

## Learning objective
To recognize and match different 2-D shapes.

## Group size
Two to four children.

## What you need
The photocopiable sheet (copied or glued onto thin card) and a short pencil for each child plus one for yourself; scissors; a collection of 2-D shapes.

## Preparation
Colour, cut out and make a spinner, pushing the pencil through the centre to make a spindle.

## What to do
Let the children handle and look at the shapes. Hold up a circle and ask them to think of things that are circular. Encourage them to look around for ideas. Repeat with each of the other shapes, taking care to point out the particular attributes. Carefully count the corners and sides together. Demonstrate to the children that a square's sides are all the same length, but a rectangle has opposite sides the same length. Hold up individual shapes and let the children take turns to say the shape's name.

## Individual task
Demonstrate your spinner and how it points to a different shape after each spin. Give each child a copy of the photocopiable sheet. Let them colour in the spinner shapes. Help them to cut it out and make it by pushing a pencil through the middle. Invite them to take turns with their spinner, naming the shape it comes to rest on. Make a tick on the shape if they name it correctly. Ask them to choose a matching shape. Let them count up the shapes to see who has won! Lie the spinner flat and ask each child to

name the shapes. If they know them, tick each one strongly again.

## Support
After each spin ask them to find a matching shape. Help them by repeating the names and pointing out the attributes.

## Extension
Draw more complicated shapes on the reverse side of the spinner (such as rhombus, semicircle, hexagon, octagon) and repeat the game.

## Assessment
Name and keep each child's spinner. The ticks will indicate their knowledge of the shape names. The game can then be replayed at a later date to check on progress.

## Home links
Ask parents to play 'I Spy' different shapes at home or when they are out with their child.

# Spin the shape

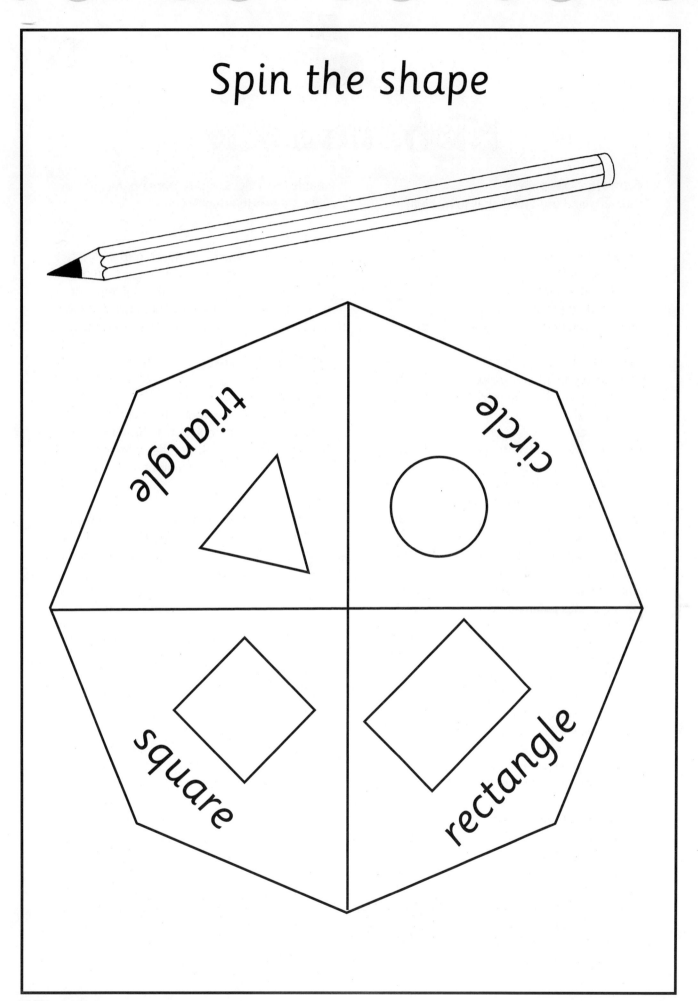

# Night and day

## Learning objective
To identify and use 2-D shapes to make a mobile.

## Group size
Two to six children.

## What you need
The photocopiable sheet (enlarged and copied onto card) and a wire coat-hanger for each child; scissors; felt-tipped pens and crayons; glue; thin card; different-coloured glitter; thread for hanging; a collection of 2-D shapes.

## What to do
Let the children look at the selection of shapes. Do they know their names? Let them match similar shapes and help them to use the correct names. Give each child a copy of the photocopiable sheet and ask them to look at the pictures. Talk about the symbols. Explain that the moon is really the same shape as the sun but that it changes when part of it is in shadow. Hold up different 2-D shapes in turn and ask them to find the same sort of shape on their sheet. Let them cut out the shapes and decorate them with the glitter. Punch a hole in each shape, and ask them to choose where to fix it on the hanger. Help them to tie each one in place. Suspend the hangers to display them.

## Individual task
After the shapes have been tied onto each child's hanger, ask them to point to the different shapes and name them. Write the date on the back of any shapes they

identify correctly. To check learning, repeat the process when the display comes down.

## Support
Talk about the shapes, pointing to triangles, circles and squares and encouraging them to repeat the correct name. Let the children sort them into sets of the same shape. Cut out the night and day symbols in advance. Help the children to match shapes from your collection to the shapes on their sun, moon and star symbols.

## Extension
Let the children draw round their cut-out shapes and make an additional mobile. Instead of decorating the shapes, ask the children to label them with the shape names.

## Assessment
Keep the known shapes you have dated and add these (inside plastic bags to retain the glitter) to each child's file as a record. Make a note of those they still need to learn and plan other shape recognition reinforcement games, such as 'I spy … a circle'.

## Home links
Ask parents to help their child to make a shape collection at home, such as a collection of circular things – buttons, lids and plates. Invite the children to bring these to school to share with others and display them.

# Night and day

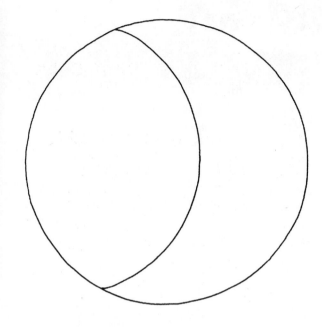

Moon

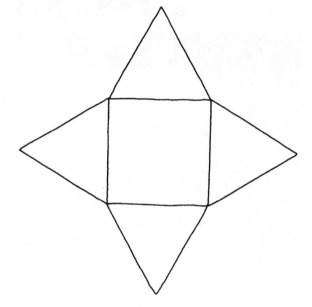

Star

Sun

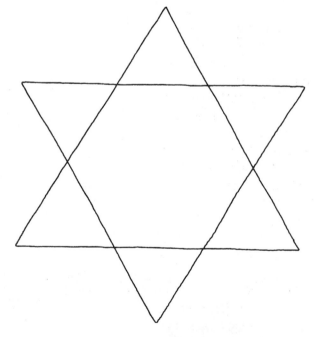

Star

# Chinese puzzle

## Learning objective
To reinforce knowledge and understanding of different 2-D shapes.

## Group size
Two to eight children.

## What you need
The photocopiable sheet (glued or copied onto card) and a piece of A4 paper each; felt-tipped pens or crayons; glue; scissors.

## What to do
Give each child a photocopiable sheet. Tell the children about Chinese Tangram puzzles – an ancient game comprising a square cut into seven pieces which can be used to make different shapes and patterns. Demonstrate how to cut out the tangram, placing the pieces on the table in the overall square shape and discussing the correct names of each shape you cut.

## Individual recording
Let each child colour in their shapes and cut out the square. Help them to cut out the shape pieces. Ask them to arrange the pieces and glue them to the paper to make their own picture, encouraging them to talk about the shapes they are using. Ask each child to count and name the different shapes and the total number of pieces on their picture. Write down their answers and their title for the picture.

## Support
Enlarge the photocopiable sheet and help the children to cut out the pieces. Look at the 2-D shapes and talk about the differences between them. Count the sides and corners of each shape and repeat the correct name. Help the children to sort and count all the triangles, squares and rectangles. Hold up the shapes in turn and play a recognition game to find out which they can recall and name.

## Extension
After the children have made their pictures, ask them to label all the different shapes. Provide them with a selection of 2-D shapes and ask them to match and reproduce it correctly.

## Assessment
Retain and date each child's picture. Make a note of the shapes that are known and those that need further work. Use the picture again at a later date to check progress, dating it and writing in a different colour.

## Home links
Make up small packs of sticky paper 2-D shapes in plastic bags and send them home with the children. Ask parents to help their child to stick these down to make different patterns and pictures. What does the child want to say about her picture? Ask the parents to write down their child's sentence.

# Chinese puzzle

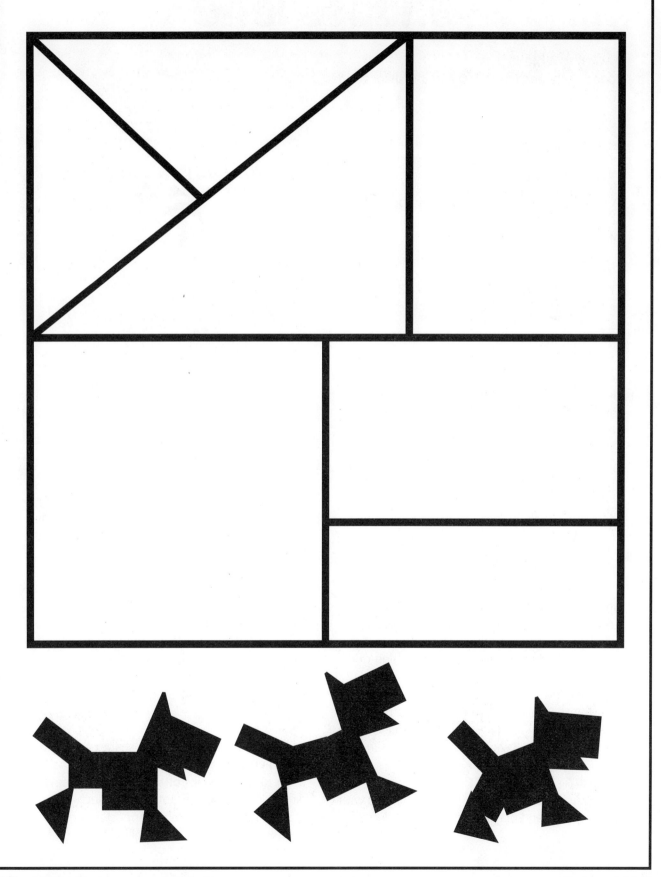

# Shapes lotto

## Learning objective
To recognize and match 2-D and 3-D shapes and solids.

## Group size
Two to four children.

## What you need
A lotto grid for each child (each photocopiable sheet provides four grids); counters; a collection of 2-D and 3-D shapes and solids.

## Preparation
Enlarge the photocopiable sheet to A3-size. Cut out the lotto grids – one for each child.

## What to do
Show the children your collection of shapes and solids. Let them feel each one, and help them to describe them. Show them the pictures on the lotto grids and demonstrate how some of the shapes match the pictures. Give each child a lotto grid and six counters. Explain that you are going to play a game of lotto and that you will show them different shapes and solids which they must look at carefully. If they have a matching shape on their lotto card then they must put a counter on it.

## Individual task
Play the game, producing one shape at a time and drawing attention to its attributes – sides, corners, two- or three-dimensional qualities. Help the children with the first few shapes. Let the children discuss who has the matching grid. Ask them to explain how they know a shape matches one on the grid. How did they check? Tick the shapes on the grid for each attribute they know such as name, general shape, sides, corners, an everyday object of the same form.

## Support
Use only 2-D shapes (cover the 3-D pictures with sticky paper) and play the game with individuals or pairs.

## Extension
Let the children take turns to lead the game by producing the shapes and solids and checking the answers before letting the others place their counter.

## Assessment
Retain, date and name the ticked lotto sheets. Where children are not sure of their shapes and solids, observe carefully and note their problem areas. Plan more matching and naming activities to meet specific needs. Repeat the game later to reinforce the children's knowledge and understanding and to check on progress.

## Home links
Encourage parents to discuss shapes and solids with their child when they are shopping. Ask them to send in a list of the two- and three-dimensional shapes that they saw (such as a square sign and a rectangular poster; a cuboid cardboard box and a spherical ball).

# Shapes lotto

# Tessellate

### Learning objective
To investigate which shapes tessellate in patterns.

### Group size
Two to six children.

### What you need
A copy of the photocopiable sheet and some paper for each child; crayons or felt-tipped pens; scissors; glue; two card strips.

### Preparation
Cut out the different shapes from a copy of the photocopiable sheet. Write 'tessellates' and 'will not tessellate' on the card strips.

### What to do
Draw the children's attention to the floor and wall patterns around you (tiles, carpet, brickwork and so on). What shapes are in the patterns? Show the children your cut-out shapes and ask them to name them. Pick a shape that tessellates well and explain that you are going to see if you can fit some of them together exactly, with no spaces between them. Make a pattern. Repeat with a circle and show the children the spaces. Put the 'tessellates' and 'will not tessellate' cards on the table and talk about what they mean. Try out some other shapes together and help the children to decide whether they tessellate or not. Which card should they go with?

### Individual recording
Invite the children to colour and cut out their own shapes. Let them try to make simple tessellating patterns with the shapes. Glue each separate pattern to paper. Ask them to tell you whether or not they fit together exactly and help them to decide which card they go with.

### Support
Use only shapes that will tessellate, introduce others at a later date. Do lots of work with plastic shapes before using the cut-out paper ones. Young children will need help to cut out the shapes, in particular, the circles.

### Extension
When the children are confident with the concept of tessellation, let them use a mixture of 2-D shapes to make patterns.

### Assessment
Listen and observe carefully to note the children's understanding of the concept of tessellation. Make a 'Book of Patterns' from the children's work and ask children to tell you which patterns in the book tessellate and which do not, asking them to explain why.

### Home links
Ask parents to look with their child at tile and brick patterns on floors, paths, pavements and walls, talking about how the different shapes fit together.

# Tessellate

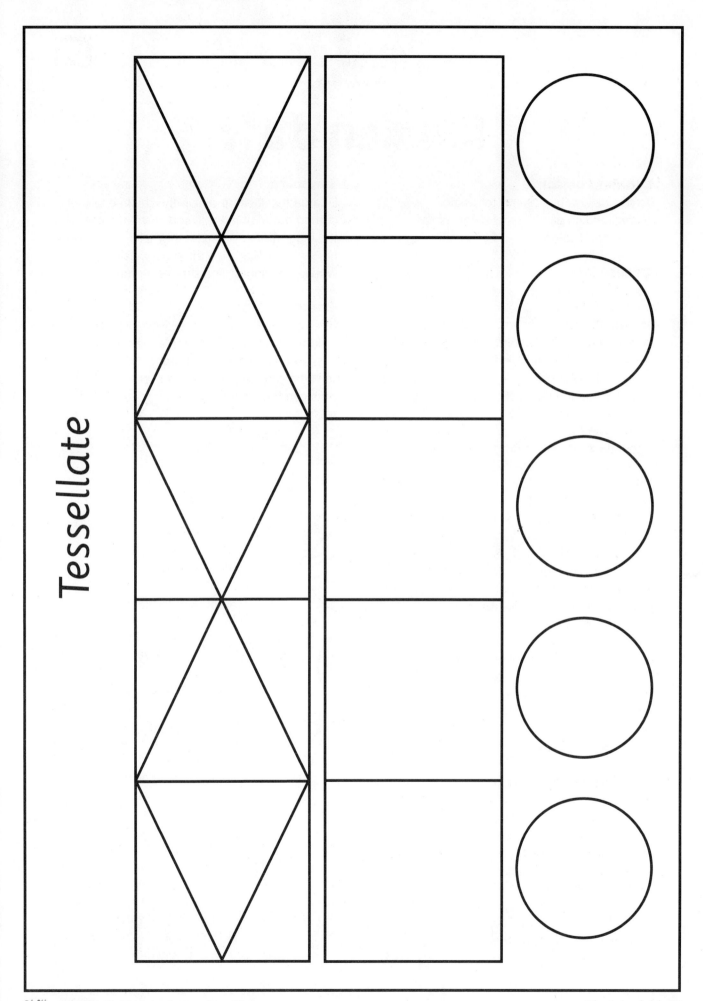

# Russian dolls

### Learning objective
To sort objects by size and to develop understanding of the terms bigger, smaller, smallest and so on.

### Group size
Four to six children.

### What you need
A collection of dolls of different sizes, including Russian dolls if possible; different-sized cars; a copy of the photocopiable sheet for each child; paper; colouring materials; scissors and glue.

### What to do
Show the children the dolls and talk about their different sizes. Help the children sort them into size order starting with the biggest. Ask: 'Is this bigger than this doll?', 'Which is the biggest/smallest?' and 'Which one is smaller than this?'. Be sure to let them compare the sizes. Repeat with the cars. If possible, show the children how Russian dolls get smaller and fit inside each other. Explain how we know they must be smaller, or they would not fit inside each other properly. Allow plenty of discussion about size differences.

### Individual recording
Give each child a copy of the photocopiable sheet. Ask them to colour each doll the same. Encourage the children to cut the dolls out and sort them into order with the biggest first. Put them in a line on the table. Now ask them to choose the biggest and then glue the next biggest on top of it. Repeat the process until all the dolls are on top of the first doll.

### Support
Enlarge the sheet and help the children with the cutting out. Ask them to sort them in a line with the biggest first. How can they tell if each one is bigger or smaller than the others? Talk about who is the biggest and smallest in their families.

### Extension
After completing the first activity, invite the children to draw and assemble their own Russian dolls. Count and number the dolls and see who can make the biggest set. How can they make their set bigger?

### Assessment
Check that the children can make size comparisons correctly and that they can use the appropriate language. Ask them to give reasons for their ideas. If they find the activity difficult, their reasons will help you pinpoint the problem and will enable you to plan further activities to help them understand size differences.

### Home links
Ask parents to help their child to sort everyday objects at home by size. Ideas include: tins and packets; fruit and vegetables; books and toys. Encourage the children to compare the size of different family members! Have a 'Big, bigger, biggest' week and ask parents to send in three similar things of very different sizes.

# Russian dolls

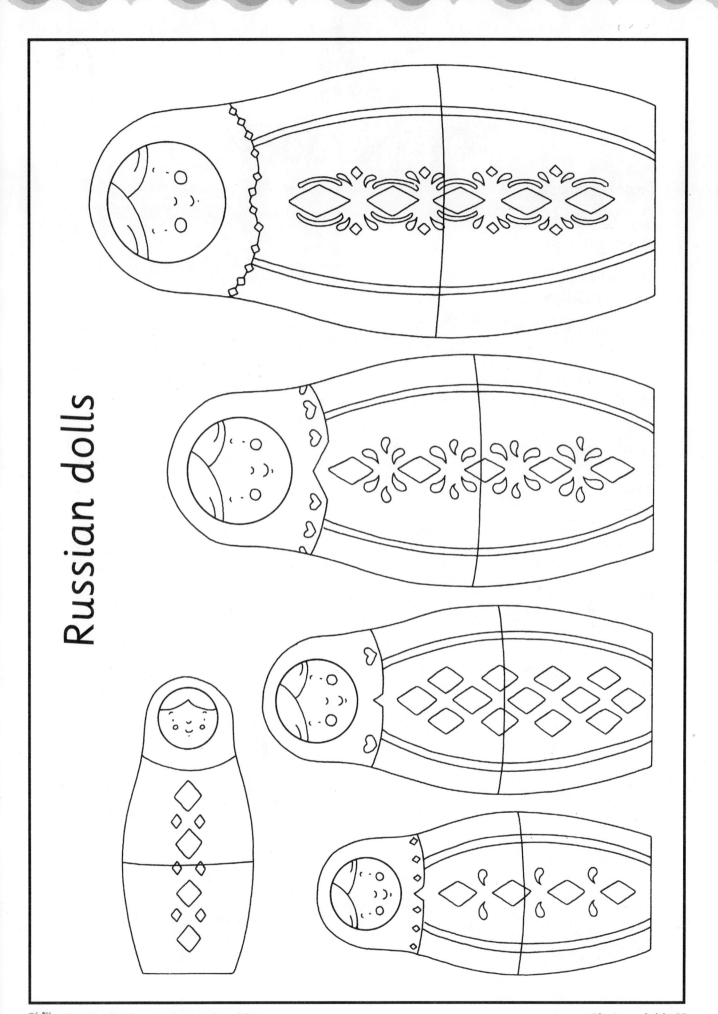

# On parade!

## Learning objective
To order different objects according to size.

## Group size
Two to six children.

## What you need
A copy of the photocopiable sheet for each child; colouring materials; scissors; paper; glue; a collection of everyday objects of different sizes; two pieces of card.

## What to do
Show the children your collection of objects and talk about the different sizes. Ask them to pick out the largest, then the smallest. Place these apart on a surface. Pick up another object and ask them to say if it is larger or smaller than the others, placing it between the first two. Repeat with the other objects, discussing the relative size of the objects and placing them in the correct order. Ask: 'Is it larger than this one?', 'Is it smaller than this one?'. Clear the surface and let the children take turns to put the objects in order again, discussing their relative sizes as they arrange them.

## Individual recording
Give each child a photocopiable sheet and let them colour and cut out the objects. Write the word 'largest' on a piece of card and put it on one side of the surface. Write the word 'smallest' on another piece of card and put it at the other end of the surface. Invite the children to sort out the pictures in order of size, starting with the largest. Let them glue them in this order on a piece of paper.

## Support
Let the children go outside, or look out of a window, and talk about the things they can see and their relative sizes. Ask: 'What is the largest thing you can see?' and 'What things are smaller than that?'.

## Extension
Ask the children to copy the words 'largest' and 'smallest' onto their piece of paper. Before they stick their pictures down, ask them to draw, cut out and add some of their own different-sized objects to the collection.

## Assessment
Check that the children can identify different sizes in comparison to other objects, using 'larger than/smaller than' correctly. Ask them to give reasons for their size order to see how their mathematical thinking and language is developing. Make a brief, dated note on their sheet of what they do and don't understand.

## Home links
Let parents know that you are looking at ordering objects by size. Ask them to play a similar game with their child, ordering toys, games and books.

# On parade!

# Long and short

### Learning objective
To identify relative size in long and short objects.

### Group size
Two to eight children.

### What you need
A copy of the photocopiable sheet for each child; scissors; colouring materials; glue; two large sheets of paper; a collection of objects of clearly different lengths.

### Preparation
Title one large sheet 'Long things' and the other 'Short things'.

### What to do
Show the children your collection of objects. Talk about long and short lengths and ask the children: 'Is this one long or short?'. Introduce the titled sheets and explain that they are going to sort the objects into sets of long and short things. Hold up each object in turn and ask the children which set it should go in – 'long things' or 'short things'. Sort all the objects, reinforcing the idea of long and short.

### Individual recording
Invite the children to colour and cut out the objects from the sheet. Ask each child to place their objects in the correct set on the paper, giving reasons for their choice. Let them glue the objects in place.

### Support
Enlarge the photocopiable sheet and help them to cut out the illustrations. Ask the children to look carefully and put the longest thing on the table. Talk about the pencil, snake and ruler and say: 'If the snake was stretched out straight, would it be longer or shorter than the pencil/ruler?'. Show the children how to use a piece of string to measure the length of the objects. Measure each one with the children and cut off the string. Compare the different lengths.

### Extension
Ask the children to sort the objects into size order, starting with the longest. Suggest that they cut out pictures from old catalogues and magazines and make their own sets of long and short items.

### Assessment
Observe the children's sorting carefully, particularly listening to their reasons for choosing a set. Make a dated note of the results by keeping the completed sets with a comment on which children understood relative length differences.

### Home links
Tell parents that you are learning about length. Ask them to help their child to sort out the family's shoes according to length. Suggest that they make a height chart by sticking tiny adhesive labels on a door frame to mark family and visitors' heights. Encourage them to talk about the differences with their child.

# Long and short

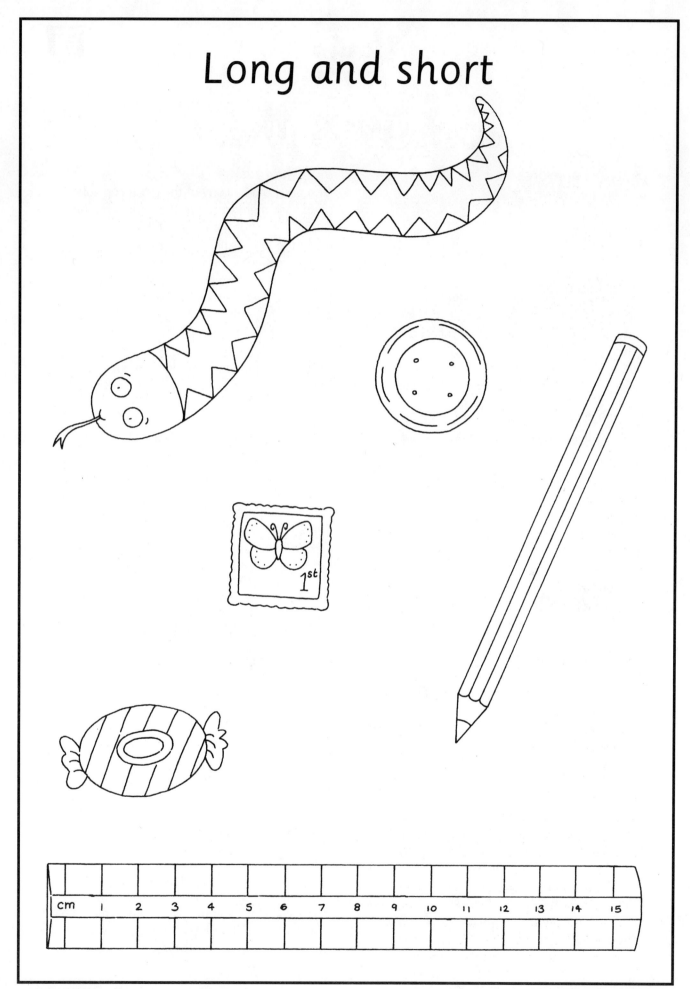

# A good fit

## Learning objective
To estimate relative sizes.

## Group size
Two to six children.

## What you need
An enlarged photocopiable sheet (glued or copied onto thin card) for each child; colouring materials; scissors; paper clips; a collection of different-sized, undressed dolls with their clothes.

## What to do
Show the children the dolls and talk about their different sizes. Look at the clothes they are wearing. Try to dress a small doll in clothes that are too large and a large doll in tiny clothes. Ask the children why they don't fit. Invite them to choose clothes that fit properly. Test their choices and talk about whether the doll needed larger- or smaller-sized clothes.

## Individual task
Give each child a copy of the photocopiable sheet. Ask them to colour the figure and the clothes, then cut them out – taking care to retain the tabs. Explain that you are going to play a dressing game together. Tell the children that they must take it in turns to hold up their figure and select an item of clothing that they think will fit. Help them to fasten each item on using the tabs (if this is difficult, attach it with paper clips). Talk about why each item fits or doesn't fit. The game finishes when all the figures are dressed.

## Support
Put two different-sized dolls on the table with a mixed-up selection of clothes to fit them. Help the children to sort the clothes into two piles to fit each doll. Talk about the different sizes, stressing 'too big', 'too small' or 'just right' as appropriate. Mix all the clothes up again and then hold up an item, asking each child in turn to match it to a doll. Provide as much help as necessary to cut out the figure and clothes on the photocopiable sheet and also give some guidance with the tabs.

## Extension
Invite the children to use the proper fitting clothes as a template to draw around. Encourage them to design and make some different clothes for their figure.

## Assessment
On each child's figure, make a note of how well they could match the correctly-sized clothes. Retain this note for their records and to assist your planning.

## Home links
Write a version of the story of 'Goldilocks and the Three Bears'. Photocopy it and give a copy to the children's parents. Ask them to read the story to their children, talking especially about the different-sized bears and their furniture.

# A good fit

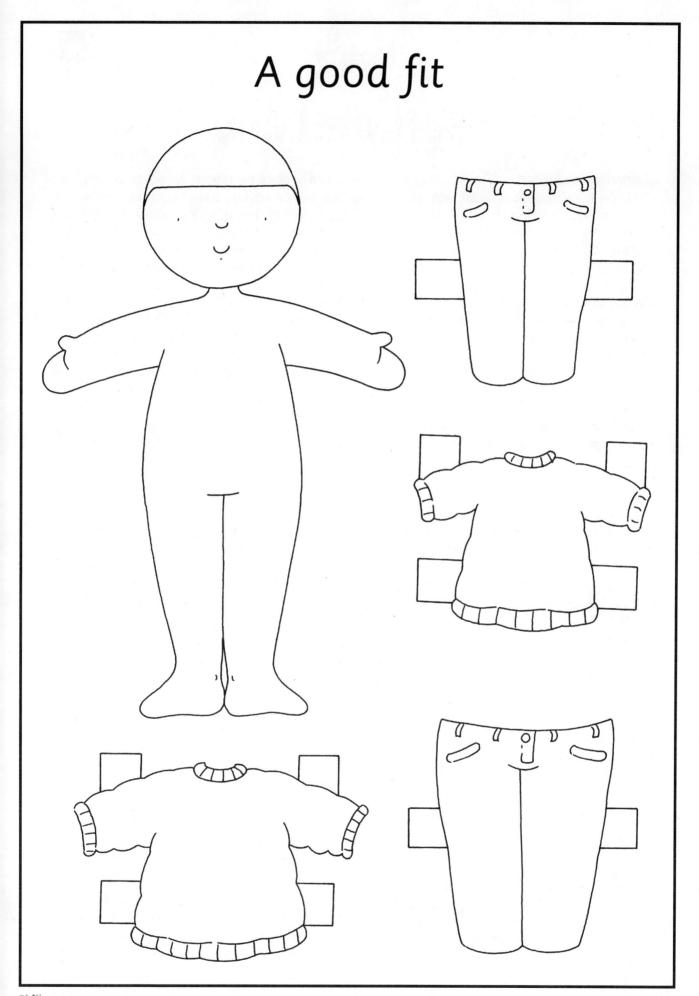

# High and low

### Learning objective
To know the difference between high up, medium height and low down.

### Group size
Three to five children.

### What you need
Two shoe boxes (without lids); glue/sticky tape; a collection of small objects; a copy of the photocopiable sheet for each child; colouring materials; scissors and glue.

### Preparation
Make simple shelves by sticking the two shoe boxes together on their side.

### What to do
Show the children the shelves and point out the high top shelf, the medium middle shelf and the low bottom shelf. Pick up an object and ask: 'Shall we put it high, medium or low?' then place it as they decide. Next, ask the children in

turn to place the objects as you direct them. Then let them take turns to put the objects where they choose, telling you whether it is high up, medium height or low down. Ask: 'Which things are higher/lower than yours?' and constantly compare their relative heights.

### Individual recording
Give each child a copy of the photocopiable sheet and invite them to colour and cut out the objects. Ask them to follow your instructions and place an object on the high, medium or low shelf as you decide. Encourage the children to stick them in place. When all the objects have been stuck down, point to each one and ask them to tell you whether it is high up, medium height or low down.

### Support
Help the children to cut out the objects. Ask them only to choose high or low shelves.

### Extension
Encourage the children to label their stuck down objects with an 'h', 'm' or 'l'. Suggest that they add and label some extra objects cut out from magazines and catalogues.

### Assessment
Check that the children can follow your directions to place objects and that they can point correctly to high, medium and low shelves. Ask which objects are the highest and lowest and which are higher/lower than others. Make a note of secure understanding and be aware of any child who is confused in order to plan further similar work to reinforce learning.

### Home links
Ask parents to reinforce the concept of high and low by talking about going higher and going lower as they go up and down the stairs with their child, and by talking about which things on supermarket shelves or bookcases are high up, medium height or low down.

# High and low

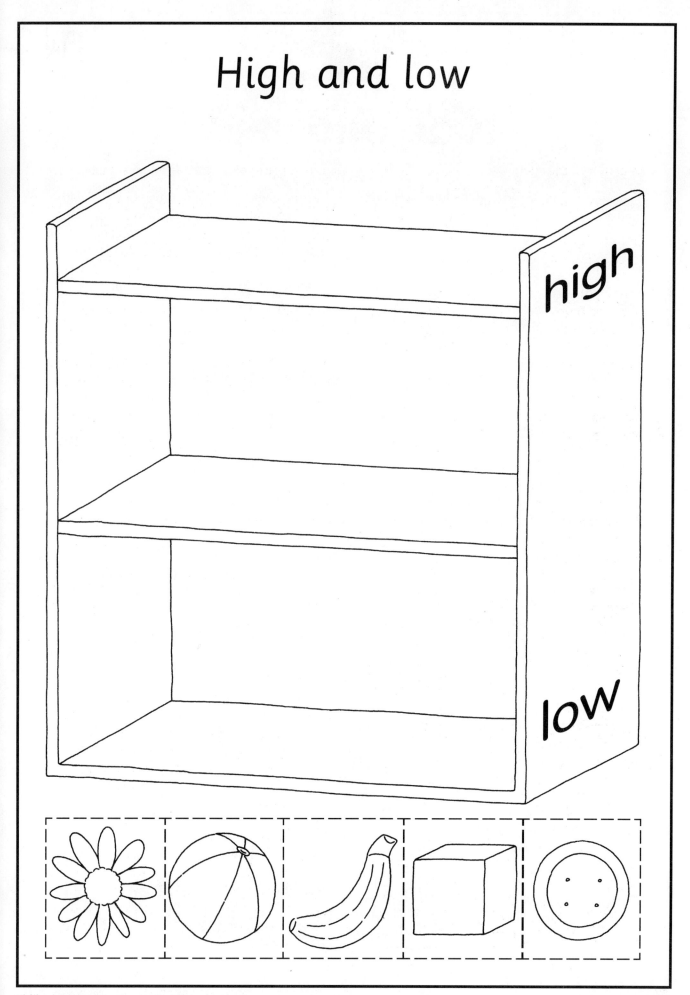

# Hide and seek

### Learning objective
To recognize and understand the terms 'on' and 'under'.

### Group size
Two to four children.

### What you need
An enlarged photocopiable sheet and a button for each child; counters; a dice with the written numerals 1–6; doll's house table, chair; cupboard and so on; a small doll (to scale).

### What to do
Show the children the doll's house furniture and the doll. Place the doll on an item and ask the children where it is. Repeat with the doll under another item. Stress 'on' and 'under'. In turn, ask the children to choose different furniture and place the doll as you direct.

### Individual task
Give each child a copy of the photocopiable sheet. Tell them you are going to play a game about 'on and under'. Allocate a handful of counters and a button to each child. Let the children take turns to throw the dice and move their button along the 'board'. If they land on a square marked 'on' or 'under', they must take a counter and place it as directed, 'on' or 'under' a piece of furniture on the board. Check that they have placed it in the right position, helping them to correct any errors. At the end of the game count up the counters to see who has the most.

### Support
Play the game in a group of two or three, with just one board. Use a dice with 1–3 spots and help the children to count the correct number of spaces. Read the words together and let the children talk about where they will place their counter first, to reinforce the concept.

### Extension
Let the children play in pairs, using different-coloured counters. Stick white labels over some of the squares and introduce additional language such as next to and behind.

### Assessment
Tick each correct placement on the sheet, date it and keep it as a record. Let the children play the game at a later date for you to check their progress and to reinforce the concept. Date and tick the sheet in a different colour.

### Home links
Suggest parents play an 'on and under' game with their child at home. Write out simple directions for them, explaining how to play a version of 'Simon Says' by propping up a tray on some tins and asking their child to put objects on or under the tray when 'Simon says'!

# Hide and seek

# Frog pond

### Learning objective
To learn the positional language of 'behind', 'in front' and 'beside'.

### Group size
Two to four children.

### What you need
A photocopiable sheet (enlarged if possible) for each child – plus one for yourself; colouring materials; scissors; glue.

### Preparation
Prepare your own copy of the sheet. Cut off the frog strips. Cut out the lily pad strips and stick them together in one long line, in number order.

### What to do
Show the children your prepared photocopiable sheet and explain to them that you are going to play a game of putting the frogs where they want to jump. Cut out your frog squares and take the first one, reading out the words 'in front'. Place a frog in front of a lily pad and ask the children to describe where he is, such as 'in front of lily pad number one'. Repeat the activity with the other frogs and positions. Let each child in turn select a position and place a frog, saying where it is.

### Individual recording
Give each child a copy of the photocopiable sheet and ask them to cut off the frog strips and create a lily pad number line. Invite them to cut

off a frog square and help them to read the position. Encourage them to select a lily pad and glue the frog into the right position. Repeat with all the frogs.

### Support
Pre-cut the frogs without the word sections and limit the positions for the children to describe 'on the lily pad' and 'in the water'.

### Extension
Let the children write the positions onto the lily pad nearest to each frog. Ask them to draw some fish, saying where they are using positional language.

### Assessment
Name and date the children's work. Make a note of how well they understood the different terms. Are they confident with the use of all the expressions? Which ones do they need further work on? Return to the game at a later date to assess progress. Reinforce the positional language with a game of 'Simon Says'. For example, 'Simon says put your hand beside your leg/on top of your head/in front of your face' and so on.

### Home links
Ask parents to let their child help lay the table or trays at home, following simple instructions such as, 'Put the mug beside the plate; put the spoon in front of the plate; put the cornflakes behind the milk jug'.

# Frog pond

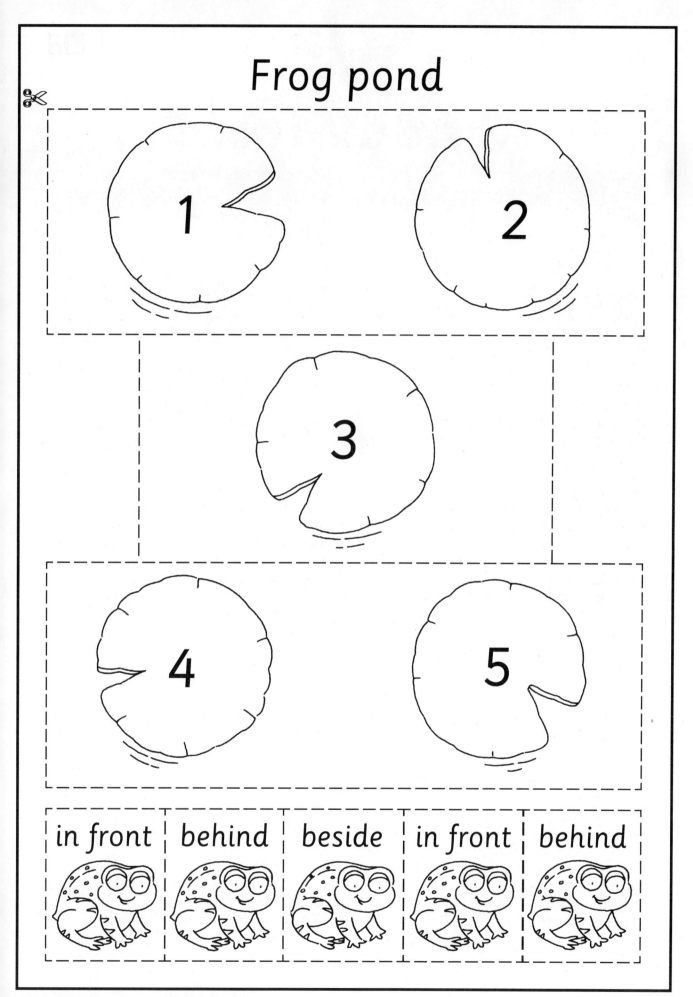

| in front | behind | beside | in front | behind |

# Where am I now?

## Learning objective
To use correct positional language to describe a location.

## Group size
Two to six children.

## What you need
A photocopiable sheet for each child, plus one for yourself; counters; Plasticine; cocktail sticks; sticky labels; pencils; a collection of small objects.

## Preparation
Enlarge the photocopiable sheets to A3-size if possible. Make a small flag for each child by fastening a sticky label round a cocktail stick, writing their name on it, then sticking it into a Plasticine base to make it stand upright.

## What to do
Arrange the objects, well-spaced out, on a suface. Show the children a counter. Ask them to close their eyes, then put it near to an object. Ask them to open their eyes and describe where it is. Stress the correct use of a range of positional language, including more than one description, such as 'in front of the car, behind the box'. Repeat and let the children hide the counter, describing its position to help you find it. Ask questions such as: 'Is it close to the doll? Is it behind the flower?' and so on.

## Individual task
Give each child a copy of the photocopiable sheet and their flag. Ask them to put their flag on the map. In turn, each child describes where they are, using positional language. When they have described the position of their flag correctly, give them a counter. Repeat the activity several times.

## Support
Help the children with questions such as: 'Is it closer to the tree or the house? Is it next to the car or the shop?'.

## Extension
After practising with the flags, let the children work in pairs, with a screen or book between them. Ask the children to take it in turns to place and describe their flag. Can their partner put it in the same position by following the other child's directions?

## Assessment
Observe and listen carefully and note any positional language that each child finds difficult. Use this information to plan further work, such as help to understand the terms near, nearer and nearest.

## Home links
Suggest parents play 'Hunt the Slipper' at home with their child, taking turns to hide a slipper somewhere in a room and giving directions, using positional language, to help the seeker find its hiding place.

# Where am I now?

# Well matched

## Learning objective
To match and make simple symmetrical patterns.

## Group size
Two to six children.

## What you need
A photocopiable sheet for each child (enlarged to A3-size if possible); colouring materials; pictures of butterflies showing wing patterns; a safety mirror; a hole punch; thread; scissors; a small twiggy branch in a pot of soil/sand.

## What to do
Show the children pictures of butterflies and how both wing patterns match. Put the mirror along the body of the butterflies and let the children see how the reflection makes a matching patterned wing. Introduce the word 'symmetry' and explain how each half must match exactly to be 'symmetrical'.

## Individual recording
Give each child a copy of the photocopiable sheet and ask them to colour in the half pictures. Let them use the mirror to see what the symmetrical pattern would be like. Remove the mirror and invite them to make a symmetrically-patterned wing, using the same colours as on the other wing. When complete, ask the children to cut

them out and write their names on the reverse. Help them to make holes in the insects and suspend them from the branch.

## Support
Faintly draw in matching patterns for the children to complete and colour match.

## Extension
Let the children use their insect shapes as templates to draw round. Ask them to design their own insects with symmetrical patterns.

## Assessment
Retain named and dated examples of the children's insects which demonstrate their understanding of symmetry.

## Home links
Send home large, plain insect shapes, folded down the centre line and ask parents to help their child to colour, paint or stick symmetrically-patterned wings. Encourage the children to bring them in to share and display them.

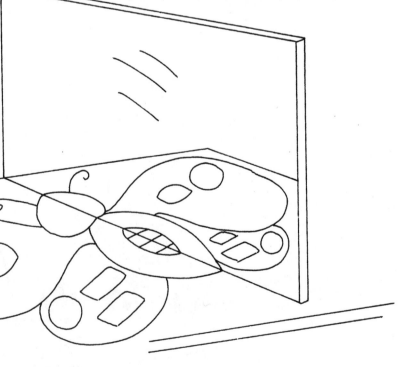

# Well matched

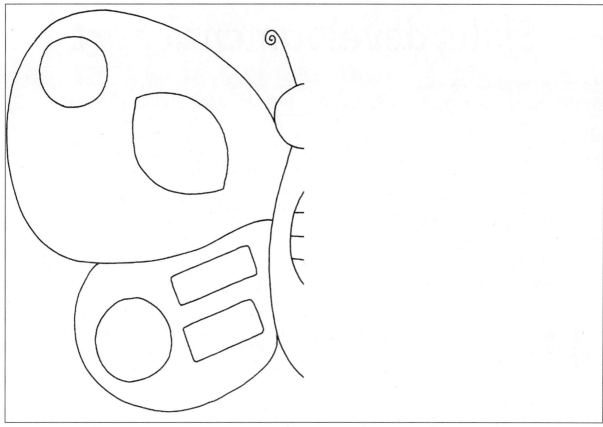

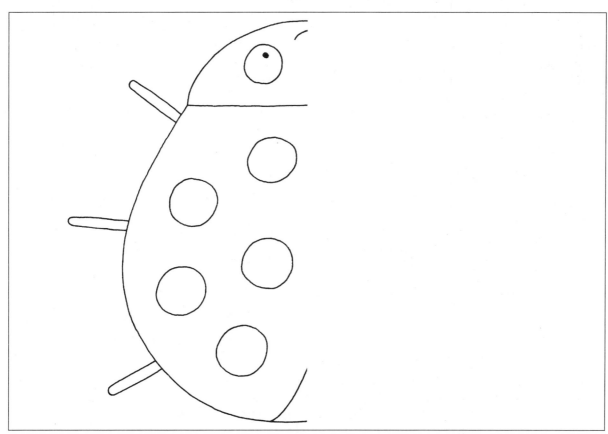

Name _____

# Skills development chart

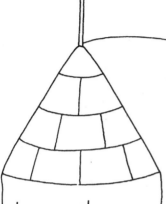

I can make simple symmetrical patterns

I know which shapes will tessellate well

I can make patterns using 2-D shapes

I can recognize and match 3-D shapes

I can recognize and match 2-D shapes

I can place objects on and under other objects following instructions

I can use correct language for behind, in front of and beside to describe position

I can recognize and place high and low objects

I can build up a pattern working from biggest to smallest

I can estimate which clothes will fit

I can recognize and sort long and short objects

I can put different objects in order of size